Piano Exam Pieces

ABRSM Grade 1

Selected from the 2013 & 2014 syllabus

Name

Date of exam

CH00336645

Contents

Editor for ABRSM: Richard Jones

Other pieces for Grade 1

† This arrangement only

First published in 2012 by ABRSM (Publishing) Ltd, a wholly owned subsidiary of ABRSM, 24 Portland Place, London W1B 1LU, United Kingdom © 2012 by The Associated Board of the Royal Schools of Music

Unauthorized photocopying is illegal All rights reserved. No part of this publication may be reproduced, recorded or transmitted in any form or by any means without the prior permission of the copyright owner.

Music origination by Julia Bovee Cover by Kate Benjamin & Andy Potts Printed in England by Headley Brothers Ltd, The Invicta Press, Ashford, Kent

MIX
Paper from responsible sources
FSC™ C109619

Minuet in G

K. 1e

DO NOT PHOTOCOPY
© MUSIC

W. A. Mozart
(1756–91)

Mozart's prodigious musical gifts were already evident when he was a small child. According to his sister Nannerl: 'He made such progress that at the age of five he was already composing little pieces, which he played to his father, who wrote them down.' This minuet was written around that time, or not long afterwards.

All dynamics and slurs are editorial suggestions only, except for the crotchet slurs in bb. 2, 4 and 10, which are present in the source. The trill in the penultimate bar is editorial.

Source: MS copy by Leopold Mozart, Museum Carolino Augusteum, Salzburg

© 1988 by The Associated Board of the Royal Schools of Music
Adapted from Mozart: *25 Early Pieces*, edited by Howard Ferguson (ABRSM)

DO NOT PHOTOCOPY
© MUSIC

Fugue

No. 4 from *Five Miniature Preludes and Fugues*

A:2

Alec Rowley
(1892–1958)

The English composer Alec Rowley studied at the Royal Academy of Music, and in 1919 became a professor at Trinity College of Music. He wrote a great deal of attractive music for educational purposes.

This brief two-part fugue opens with the subject in the tonic key, A minor, followed by its answer in the dominant key, E minor, in the left hand. A contrasting *piano* episode intervenes before the subject returns in the tonic (left hand b. 13), imitated at the upper octave (right hand b. 16). The fugue ends with a short coda.

© Copyright 1946 Chester Music Limited
All rights reserved. International copyright secured. Reprinted by permission. All enquiries about this piece, apart from those directly relating to the exams, should be addressed to Music Sales Ltd, 14–15 Berners Street, London W1T 3LJ.

Das Ballett

No. 19 from *60 Handstücke für angehende Klavierspieler*, Book 1

DO NOT PHOTOCOPY
© MUSIC

D. G. Türk
(1750–1813)

Edited by Howard Ferguson

Das Ballett The Ballet; **Handstücke für angehende Klavierspieler** Pieces for Aspiring Players

The German theorist and composer Daniel Gottlob Türk spent most of his working life in the city of Halle, where he became university music director in 1779, rising to professor of music in 1808. His two books of *60 Handstücke für angehende Klavierspieler* of 1792 and 1795 were designed for use alongside his voluminous *Clavierschule* (1789), the most influential instruction manual of its day.

In this piece, lightly detached quavers might help to convey the deft footwork of a skilled ballet dancer. The dynamic marks at the start of each strain are editorial, the others authentic.

Source: *Sechzig Handstücke für angehende Klavierspieler, Erster Theil* (Leipzig and Halle, 1792)

© 1988 by The Associated Board of the Royal Schools of Music
Reproduced from Türk: *Sixty Pieces for Aspiring Players*, Book 1, edited by Howard Ferguson (ABRSM)

DO NOT PHOTOCOPY
© MUSIC

Moderato

No. 2 from *20 malen'kikh p'es dlya nachinayushchikh*, Op. 6

B:1

A. F. Gedike
(1877–1957)

Malen'kikh p'es dlya nachinayushchikh Little Pieces for Beginners

The Russian composer Aleksandr Fyodorovich Gedike studied piano and composition at the Moscow Conservatory from 1892 to 1898, and was appointed professor of piano there in 1909. He was active as a concert pianist, both in Russia and abroad, and in 1900 his performance of his own piano concerto won first prize in the Rubinstein Competition in Vienna.

This Moderato is a short, lyrical piano piece of the type often described as a character piece. In this case there is no specific programme, but the clearly defined rhythms convey a distinctive mood. The accent in b. 10 is editorial (cf. b. 2), as are the first staccato dot in b. 12 (cf. b. 4) and the left-hand staccatos in b. 15.

Source: 20 маленьких пьес для начинающих, Op. 6 (Moscow, 1946)

© 2012 by The Associated Board of the Royal Schools of Music

B:2

Sailor's Song

No. 11 from *Work and Play*

Felix Swinstead
(1880–1959)

Quick march time [♩ = *c*.144]

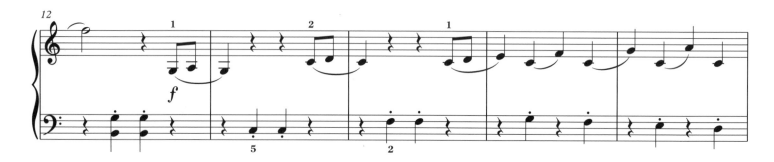

The English pianist, teacher and composer Felix Swinstead studied at the Royal Academy of Music, where he was appointed professor of piano in 1910. Before the First World War he gave many piano recitals, both in London and elsewhere, and from 1917 he was an ABRSM examiner. Most of his published works are for the piano, and many of these were written for educational purposes.

   'Sailor's Song' is written in the style of a hornpipe, a dance type often associated with sailors. Editorial staccatos have been added in the left hand of b. 3 (cf. b. 21) and b. 16 (cf. b. 15).

© 1935 by The Associated Board of the Royal Schools of Music
Reproduced from Thomas F. Dunhill: *First Year Pieces* and Felix Swinstead: *Work and Play* (ABRSM)

Na łódce

from *Zaczynam grać*, Op. 20

B:3

Feliks Rybicki
(1899–1978)

Na łódce In a Boat; **Zaczynam grać** I Begin to Play

The Polish composer Feliks Rybicki studied composition and conducting at the Warsaw Conservatory in the early 1920s. Later, he conducted the Warsaw Philharmonic Orchestra, and both wrote and directed music for the Warsaw theatres and Polish radio. Rybicki's output includes orchestral, vocal, chamber and piano music. Among the latter are a number of educational albums, including *Zaczynam grać*, Op. 20 (1946), which is widely used in elementary piano studies.

In this piece the right hand seems to convey the pleasure of the boating trip, and the left hand the gentle rocking of the boat.

© 1957 by Polskie Wydawnictwo Muzyczne SA, Kraków, Poland
All rights reserved. All enquiries about this piece, apart from those directly relating to the exams, should be addressed to Polskie Wydawnictwo Muzyczne SA, al. Krasińskiego 11a, 31–111 Kraków, Poland.

Thursday

from *Seven Days a Week*

R. R. Bennett
(born 1936)

DO NOT PHOTOCOPY
© MUSIC

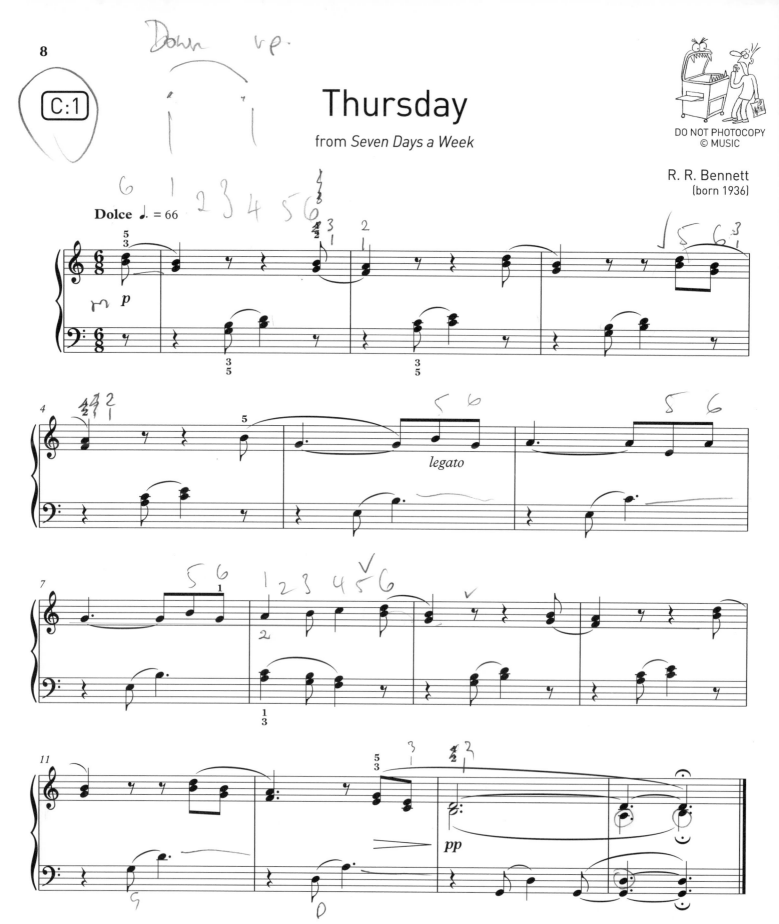

Sir Richard Rodney Bennett studied at the Royal Academy of Music (1953–6) with Howard Ferguson and Lennox Berkeley, and was then taught by Pierre Boulez in Paris for two years. Besides being a highly prolific and versatile composer, he is well known as a jazz pianist, and his strong interest in jazz often lends colour and vitality to his compositions.

'Thursday', from *Seven Days a Week*, is written for the white keys only; and since the keynote is G, this gives it a certain modal character. Although the composer's metronome mark is ♩. = 66, students may prefer a more relaxed tempo of ♩. = c.56. Either tempo would be acceptable in the exam.

© 1963 EMI MILLS MUSIC, INC.

Exclusive worldwide print rights administered by Alfred Music Publishing Co., Inc. All rights reserved. Used by permission. All enquiries about this piece, apart from those directly relating to the exams, should be addressed to Alfred Music Publishing Co., Inc., 16320 Roscoe Boulevard, Suite 100, P.O. Box 10003, Van Nuys, CA 91410-0003, USA.

DO NOT PHOTOCOPY
© MUSIC

March

No. 1 from *Detskaya tetrad'*, Op. 69

Dmitry Shostakovich
(1906–75)

C:2

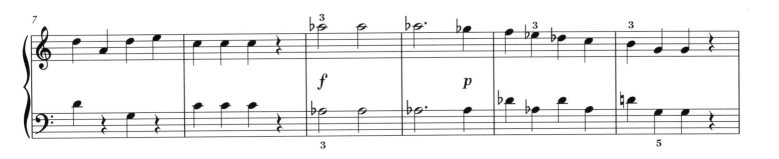

Detskaya tetrad' Children's Notebook

This march is the first of seven simple piano pieces, written during the years 1944 and 1945 by the Russian composer Dmitry Shostakovich and dedicated to his daughter Galina. She gave their first public performance in Moscow in the winter of their completion.

    All dynamics are editorial suggestions only. Most crotchets might be lightly detached, though the *piano* passages in the middle section might form a more *legato* contrast.

© Copyright 1946 Boosey & Hawkes Music Publishers Ltd for the UK, British Commonwealth (excluding Canada) and Eire
Reproduced by permission. All enquiries about this piece, apart from those directly relating to the exams, should be addressed to Boosey & Hawkes Music Publishers Ltd, Aldwych House, 71–91 Aldwych, London WC2B 4HN.

Chattanooga Choo Choo

(middle eight)

DO NOT PHOTOCOPY © MUSIC

Arranged by Mark Marshall

Harry Warren (1893–1981) and
Mack Gordon (1904–59)

This is a piano arrangement of the middle section of an American popular song, with music by Harry Warren and lyrics by Mack Gordon. It featured in the 1941 film *Sun Valley Serenade* and was recorded by Glenn Miller and his orchestra. The song tells of a long-distance train journey from New York to Chattanooga (Tennessee), hauled by a small 2-6-0 steam locomotive. The journey is described in the lyrics thus:

You leave the Pennsylvania Station 'bout a quarter to four
Read a magazine and then you're in Baltimore
Dinner in the diner
Nothing could be finer
Than to have your ham an' eggs in Carolina

When you hear the whistle blowin' eight to the bar
Then you know that Tennessee is not very far
Shovel all the coal in
Gotta keep it rollin'
Woo, woo, Chattanooga there you are

© 1941 Twentieth Century Music
All rights controlled by EMI Feist Catalog Inc. (Publishing) and Alfred Music Publishing Co., Inc. (Print). For Australia and New Zealand: J Albert & Son Pty Ltd, administered by Sasha Music Publishing, a division of All Music Publishing & Distribution Pty Ltd. All rights reserved. Used by permission. All enquiries about this piece, apart from those directly relating to the exams, should be addressed to Alfred Music Publishing Co., Inc., 16320 Roscoe Boulevard, Suite 100, P.O. Box 10003, Van Nuys, CA 91410-0003, USA.

Piano Exam Pieces

This album contains nine pieces from ABRSM's 2013 & 2014 Grade 1 Piano syllabus.

Key features:

- three pieces from each of Lists A, B and C
- appealing and varied repertoire
- carefully edited and clearly presented throughout
- helpful information about the pieces and the exam

Recordings

All of the pieces on the Grade 1 syllabus have been recorded for ABRSM by leading professional pianists. The recordings are available on CD – sold individually or as part of the *Piano Exam Pieces with CD* package – or as downloads from www.abrsm.org/audioshop.

Support material for ABRSM Piano exams

 Digital resources are also available from the ABRSM app centre: www.abrsm.org/appcentre.

ABRSM is the exam board of the Royal Schools of Music. We are committed to actively supporting high-quality music-making, learning and development throughout the world, and to producing the best possible resources for music teachers and students.

Oxford University Press is the sole worldwide sales agent and distributor for ABRSM Publishing.

ABRSM
24 Portland Place
London W1B 1LU
United Kingdom

www.abrsm.org

9781848494015
PU
07/12
E   £4.75

ISBN 978-1-84849-401-5

9 781848 494015

ABRSM
PUBLISHING

Ian Denley

Time Pieces

for
Clarinet

Music through the Ages in 3 Volumes

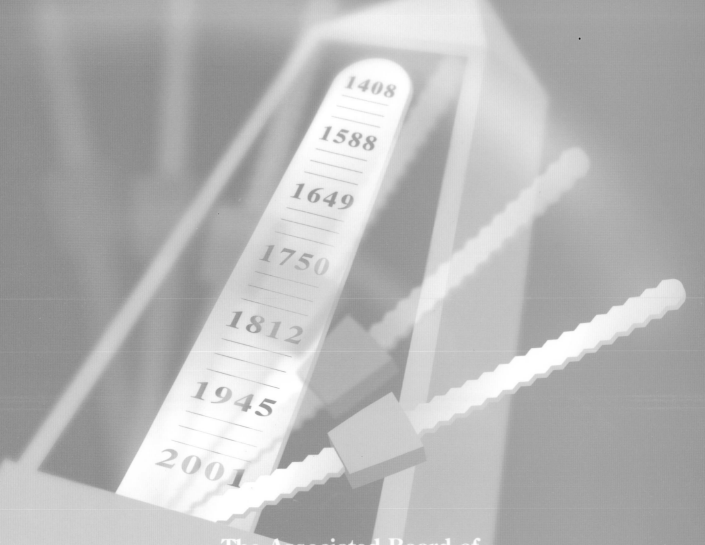

1408

1588

1649

1750

1812

1945

2001

**The Associated Board of
the Royal Schools of Music**